THE KID RETURNS

by Jarrett Mentink, Ph.D.
illustrations by Patrick Carlson

This book is dedicated to "Ma" and "Pa" — for making
all of their kids and grandkids feel like their favorite!

©2009 Jarrett W. Mentink, Ph.D. All rights reserved.

Printed in Korea, First Edition.
ISBN: 978-0-9723314-3-2

Published by Kids In The Clouds™
www.kidsintheclouds.com

Here in Seattle,
this place that we love,
With Mt. Rainier and Lake Union
and the needle above;

We once housed a hero
with an S on his lid.
His name was not needed –
He was simply, "The Kid!"

The Kid did it all –
Things never before seen.
He got his call to the M's
when he was only 19!

He could throw like Clemente
and catch baskets like Mays.
He made hard catches look
like the easiest plays.

And of course when he swung
he would hit it a mile.
The best part of all –
He did it all with a smile.

In fact it is told
his swing was so sweet,
He once had his own candy –
A milk chocolate treat!

Fans quickly heard of
his talents and skills
And they flocked to the Kingdome
to soak up the thrills.

Though 19 years old,
he was no normal rookie;
He grew up with the game –
This was one special cookie!

For The Kid wasn't new
to the major league scene.
His father had starred
for the Big Red Machine!

NOW PLAYING
THE BIG RED
MACHINE!

Ken Griffey Senior
is his dad's name.
He taught his young Junior
to play this great game.

So Junior shined bright
at a very young age.
He was ready for stardom
with no fear of the stage.

Expectations soared high
for Senior's young son.
But pops always said,
"Just go out and have fun!"

And boy did he ever,
right to the Pros,

With his bat full of thunder
and his arm like a hose.

The Kid made Seattle proud
as the draft's very first pick.
He gave gifts to the fans
that rivaled those of St. Nick!

To speak of his catches
would take the whole day,
Like up to rob Barfield
and the Spiderman play...

He once made a catch
crashing into the wall.
He injured his wrist
but did not drop the ball.

Then there's the homers
in 8 consecutive games,
Off so many pitchers
I can't remember their names!

And we all got to witness
Junior live out a dream
When the Mariners brought
his father onto the team.

Senior was no longer
the star of his prime,
Yet he and Junior made history
one day in Anaheim.

Senior launched the first missile
and said, "That's how it's done!"

Then, as a proud papa,
he watched Junior join the fun.

The only father-son tandem
to go back to back!
Another memory and record
to add to the stack.

And of course there's "The Double"
with The Kid on first base.
Junior ran like a deer
with a lion in chase.

All eyes of Seattle watched
The Kid score that run –
A dash for the ages
by our favorite son.

They'd beaten the Yanks
in the A.L.D.S. –
A baseball town in Seattle?
The answer was YES!

A new park was built
to replace the aging Kingdome.
Safeco Field was the place
for Griffey Jr. to roam.

Then in 1999
we all dropped our heads
With the news that The Kid
had been dealt to the Reds.

Yes, The Kid had left town,
but there were many who felt,
Safeco Field could be named
The House Junior Built.

Eleven years we were given
to watch Junior grow
From "The Kid" to a legend
we soaked up the show.

We watched from afar
our Kid's career,
Clinging tight to the memories
that we held so dear.

But just when it seemed
Junior had forgotten our past,
He came back to Seattle and said,
"This stop should be last."

"For my Mariner family
through all times and trials
Brought me the widest
of all of my smiles."

You see, Junior remembered
the support in the Dome,
And thought he'd say thanks
by coming back home.

So next time you're at Safeco
take a good look around.
The Kid has returned –
All is well in the Sound!